I loVe my Family

Written by Tammy Troute-Wood

Illustrated by Brent Patrick Gough

Graphic Design by Jeff Petrick

Forward by Christine Korol

How to Use this Book by Heather Cobb

 There is a heart to find
on every page.

ISBN 978-0-986̸̶ ̶ ̶

For more inforn

www.m_y̶ ̶ ̶ ̶books.com

Forward

Children that are conceived through ART (Assisted Reproductive Technologies) need a clear understanding of how they were brought into this world and to feel terrific about the many ways that families are created.

Parents need the words to guide their children at various developmental stages and to reduce their own discomfort in how this knowledge will impact their children.

Christine Korol, Ph.D.

Christine Korol, Ph.D. is a paediatric psychologist specializing in anxiety and stress in children and is currently practicing in Calgary, Alberta, Canada.

She has worked for many years, both in private practice and in hospital settings, explaining hard to understand situations to kids.

Christine is also a cartoonist and the author of the blog wiredtoworry.com

I love my family,
my family loves me.
This is a story about how
I came to be.

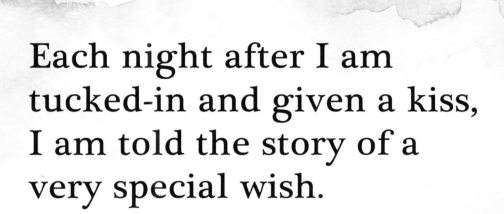

Each night after I am
tucked-in and given a kiss,
I am told the story of a
very special wish.

A wish from my family for
a dream to come true.

A dream about a child to
love, through and through.

The more my family wished...

the more they missed,

not having a child
　　to kiss
　　　　and kiss
　　　　　　and kiss.

As time passed,
life got so fast and busy…

they almost got dizzy!

But at night,
when life was quiet and still,
hope for a child began to swell.

It was then they decided a
doctor to tell, about how much
they hoped and wished…

to have a child
      to kiss
            and kiss
                 and kiss.

My family asked the doctor,
"How do we have our dreams
come true?"

The doctor explained,
"I know what to do."

If an ovum from
a woman is put with
some sperm from a man,
and it goes very well…

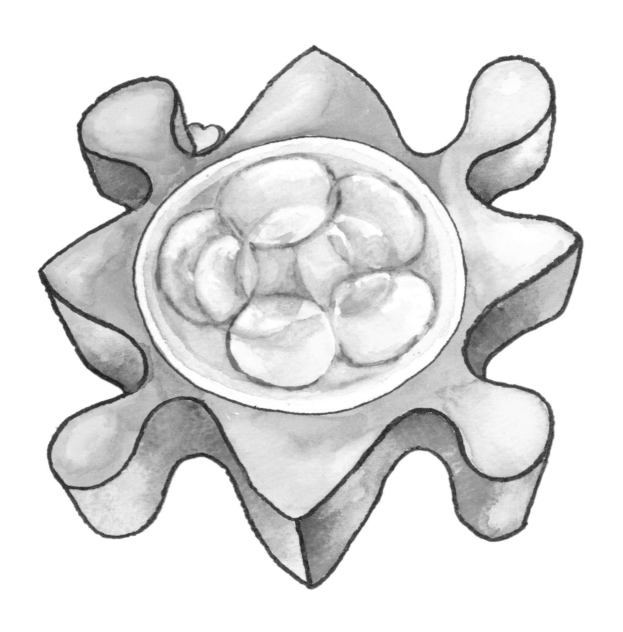

…they have the power
to form a super cell.

The super cell is called an
embryo, and when placed
inside a woman's uterus to grow,

if all the pieces have fit
together just right,

it might,
      just might,
            create a new life.

Every family is different,
this much is true;
but all families need the same
pieces of the puzzle to be glued.

The love of a family is the glue
that makes it all fit together.
It is the love of a family that
bonds you forever.

My family
became very excited,
now that the puzzle pieces
would all be united…

They might, just might,
get their hope and wish…

to have a child
    to kiss
        and kiss
           and kiss.

The doctor helped my family
an embryo to create,
but then they had
                to wait
                        and wait
                                and wait.

Only time would tell,
if it all went well...

Although they needed
some help at the start,

the love of my family came
straight from their hearts.

Now at night,
my family no longer
needs to wish, because
here I am to kiss
and kiss
and kiss!

How to use this book

When you share this book with your family consider the following tips for talking:

This is a special conversation and will be the first of many. Try to avoid making it the 'big talk'.

Familiarize yourself with the content of this book and reflect on your own feelings. Are you ready for questions? Acknowledge your feelings about assisted conception and the infertility experience. If you are having difficult emotions talk to a family member, friend or professional.

Consider talking with other family members and trusted friends before you talk to your child/ren. Consider having them read the story so they feel prepared and comfortable for a conversation that your child might initiate with them.

Choose a time and place that works best for your child. Your child may have questions that need further discussion so give yourself plenty of time to do this.

Choose a comfortable place free of distractions.

Some children may only be able to take in small amounts of information and will also need time to process this new material.

Do you have answers to questions your child may ask? Use the glossary to help you answer questions in a way that is appropriate for your family e.g., "My friend says babies grow in a mommy's tummy, so what is a uterus?"

Questions from your child may come when you least expect them, in the grocery line-up or at the playground. If your child wants to talk, use this as a 'teachable moment'. Try to answer questions in an age appropriate and direct way. Remind your child that you can both look back at this book again.

Accept that a child may decide that s/he does not want to talk at this time. You know your child best, so watch for cues from your child and scale back on your discussions accordingly. Create other opportunities to keep talking.

Use the Love, Hope, and Wishes coloring pages to keep them engaged, and help your child to understand your family story. Talk about your hopes and wishes for your family. Ask your child about their hopes and wishes.

If appropriate, use the reproductive puzzle to help explain which pieces your family needed help with.

For example:

- A male/female couple who did IVF for unexplained infertility might say "mommy and daddy had love, eggs and sperm but we needed help from the doctor to create the embryo that was put in mommy's uterus."
- An egg donor family with a male/female couple might say "mommy and daddy had love, sperm and a uterus but we needed help with eggs. The doctor helped get some eggs from another woman called a donor. We used those donor eggs and daddy's sperm to create an embryo. The embryo was put into mommy's uterus."
- A sperm donor family with a female/female couple might say "mom and mommy had love, eggs and a uterus. We needed some help from the doctor to get sperm from a man called a donor. We used the donor sperm and mommy's eggs to create an embryo. The embryo was put into mom's uterus."
- A single woman might say "mommy had love and eggs but needed help from the doctor to get sperm from a man called a donor. We used the donor sperm and my eggs to create an embryo that was put into my uterus."
- A male/female couple who used gestational surrogacy might say "mommy and daddy had love, sperm and eggs but we needed a uterus where our embryo could grow into a baby. We needed some help from the doctor to put our embryo into another woman's uterus. The woman who helped us is called a surrogate."

Share your family beliefs and values with your child. There is no right way to use the book, tell the story that fits for your family.

Enjoy using this book with your child to help put the pieces of the family puzzle together. i.e., Draw members of your family into the puzzle pieces colouring page. Talk to your child/ren about the meaning of family. What makes your family special?

By Heather Cobb, BSc, PGCE

Heather Cobb currently works as a Sexual Health Promotion Specialist in Calgary, Alberta. An education and training professional, Heather works with children and parents to help families understand and value healthy relationships and sexuality. Heather also has extensive experience teaching and developing resources for children and youth with differing abilities.

Glossary

Assisted Reproductive Technologies (ART) - fertility treatments in which the female and male reproductive cells (ovum and sperm) are handled outside the body. This includes In Vitro Fertilization (IVF) as well as donor egg and/or donor sperm and gestational surrogacy.

Embryo - earliest stage of human development after an ovum is fertilized by sperm.

Love - powerful emotion of caring and commitment for someone or something. Love is the special bond that keeps us connected.

Ovum - the medical name for a human egg which contains the female's genetic information. Also called the female reproductive cell, oocyte or female gamete.

Sperm - the name for the male reproductive cell which contains the male's genetic information. Also called the male gamete.

Uterus - the medical name for the organ of the female reproductive system where a fertilized egg (embryo) implants and develops into a fetus. Also called the womb.

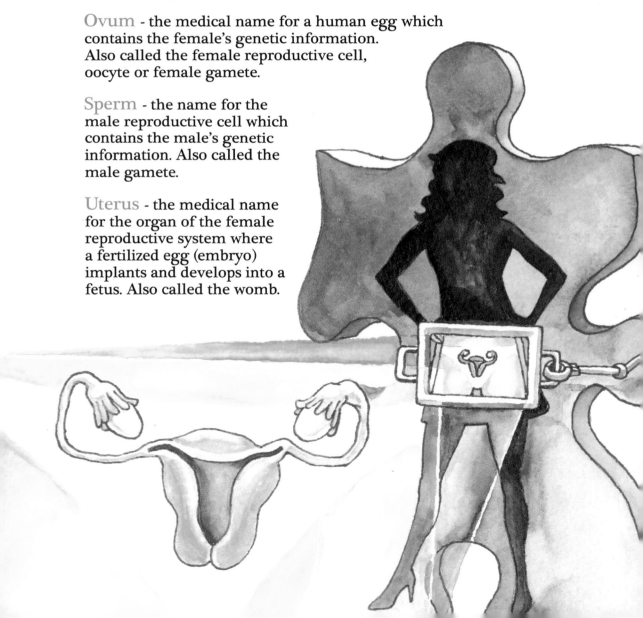

Colouring page:
LOVE

Tip: Talk about what love means to you. Ask your child what love means to them. How does your family show love to one another?

Colouring page:

HOPE

Tip: Talk about what hope and wishes means to you. What are your hopes
and wishes for your family? Ask your child about their hopes and wishes.

Colouring page:

WISHES

Tip: Talk about what hope and wishes means to you. What are your hopes and wishes for your family? Ask your child about their hopes and wishes.

Colouring page:

MY FAMILY

Tip: Decorate the puzzle pieces, cut-out from the page and use them as a tool to discuss your family. What does family mean to you? What pieces of the puzzle did you need help with? What makes your family special?

About the Author & Illustrator

Tammy Troute-Wood, RN MN currently works as a sexual and reproductive health specialist in Calgary, Alberta. Tammy has also worked as a labour and delivery nurse, family planning clinic nurse, and at the IVF clinic in Calgary. Tammy has two children conceived by InVitro Fertilization. She feels passionate about helping professionals and families increase their understanding and comfort to talk about sexual and reproductive health.

Brent Patrick Gough, BFA, BEd teaches Visual Art and Physical Education at a wonderful High School in Calgary, Alberta. A great deal of his "free" time is spent as a working musician, a Rugby Coach and an avid fly-fisherman. Much of his illustrative inspiration is drawn from his three beautiful nieces: Sara, Erin and Kira!

Made in the USA
Lexington, KY
21 August 2012